Waybuloo™

This Annual belongs to

Jasmine

Age

4

Favourite Pipling

Deli

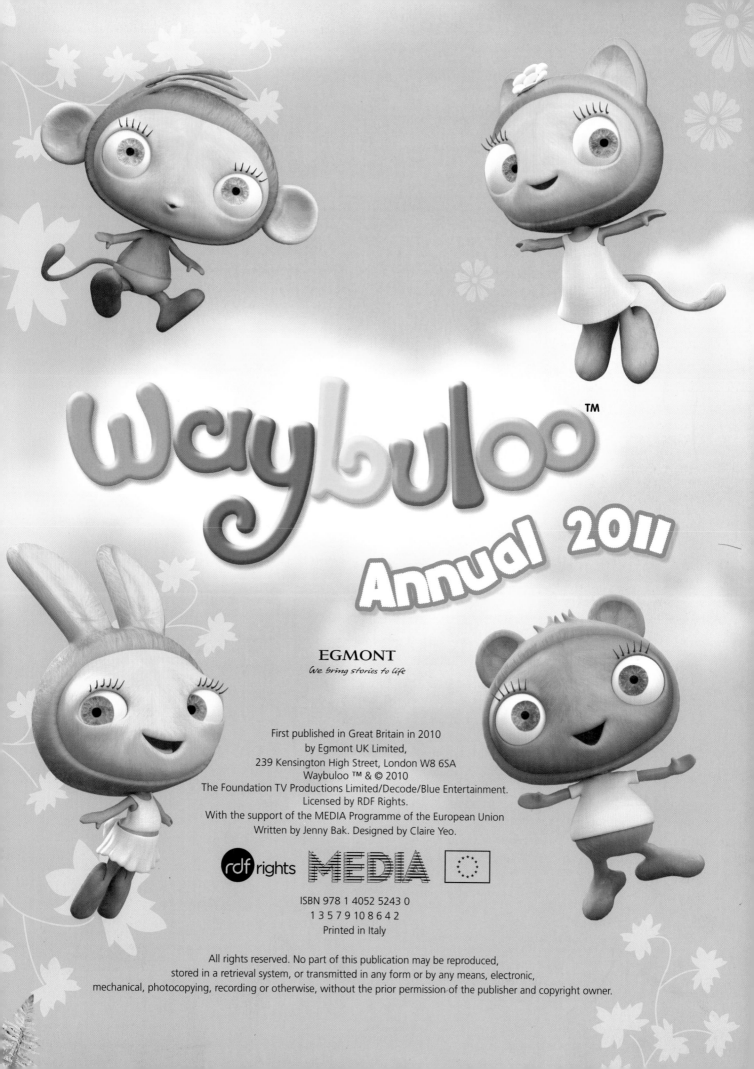

Waybuloo™

Annual 2011

EGMONT
We bring stories to life

First published in Great Britain in 2010
by Egmont UK Limited,
239 Kensington High Street, London W8 6SA
Waybuloo ™ & © 2010
The Foundation TV Productions Limited/Decode/Blue Entertainment.
Licensed by RDF Rights.
With the support of the MEDIA Programme of the European Union
Written by Jenny Bak. Designed by Claire Yeo.

rdf rights MEDIA

ISBN 978 1 4052 5243 0
1 3 5 7 9 10 8 6 4 2
Printed in Italy

Contents

Say hello to the Piplings!

You'll have lots of fun playing games, reading stories, and solving Pipling puzzles in their new annual.

Answers to puzzles are on page 68.

Come on, cheebie! Let's go!

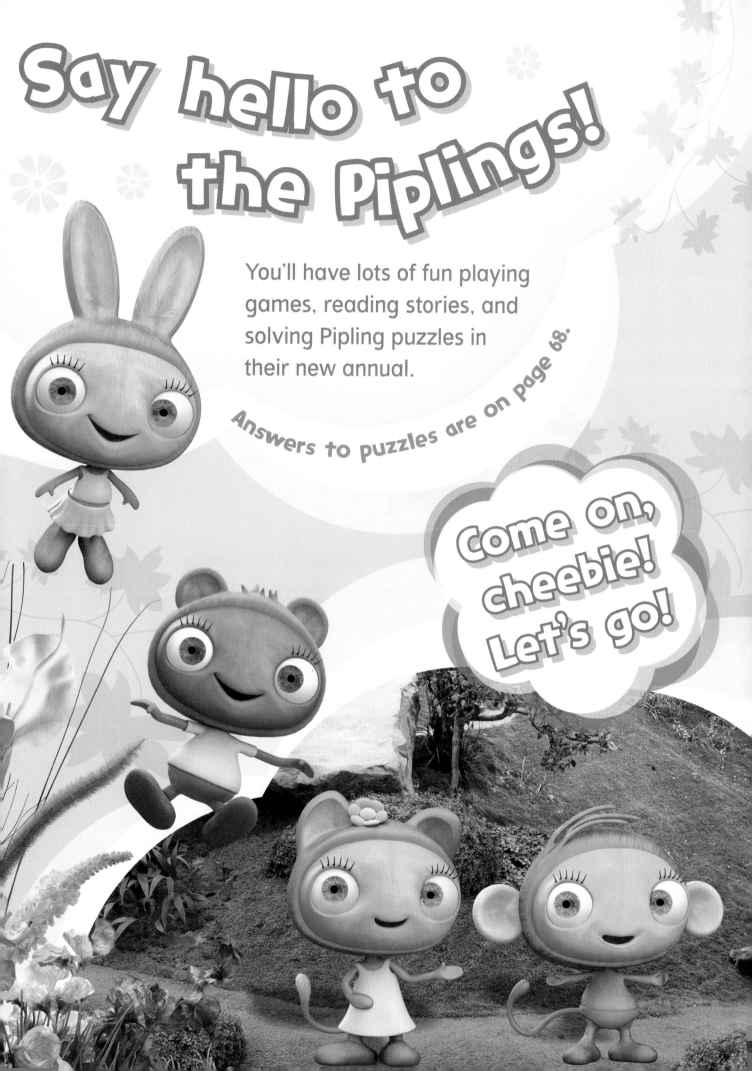

Hi Hi, Cheebie!

The Piplings live in a beautiful land called Nara. When the cheebies come to Nara, the Piplings are always ready to play! Would you like to meet them?

Yojojo

Yojojo is sweet and playful. He loves to make music for his friends. Can you pretend to play a banjojo like **Yojojo?**

Lau Lau

Lau Lau is fun and caring. She likes to dance and paint pictures. Can you show **Lau Lau** how to dance?

Nok Tok

Nok Tok is strong and helpful. He can mend or make anything with his tools. Can you pretend to bang a hammer like Nok Tok?

De Li

De Li is kind and loves to share. She grows nice things in her garden. Can you pretend to eat a strawberry like De Li?

Odd One Out

One of these pictures of **Yojojo** is different from the rest. Can you spot the odd one out?

Picture Present

Lau Lau is giving a painting to Yojojo. Can you show Lau Lau the quickest way through the maze to Yojojo's home?

start ➡

➡ finish

Draw the Piplings

Draw a happy Pipling face!

1 On a piece of paper, draw two large ovals, one inside the other, to make a head and face.

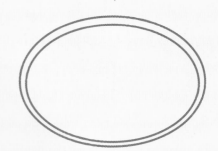

2 Add in two eyes. The eyes are three circles, one inside the other.

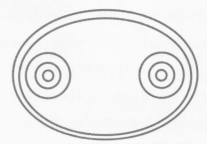

3 Don't forget the eyelashes and a big smile.

4 Lastly, draw in two ears. Look at these pictures to see what the Piplings' faces look like.

Now colour in your Pipling face!

Garden Guess

De Li grows yummy things in her garden to share with her friends. Can you tell what comes next in each row? Draw it in the box, then colour it in.

1
banana mango banana mango

2
carrobeet strawberry carrobeet strawberry

3
plumato neepnip plumato neepnip

Playing Catch

1

Yojojo, De Li and Lau Lau are playing catch. One Pipling throws the ball and another Pipling catches it. Nok Tok wants to join in!

2

But Nok Tok doesn't know how to catch. Lau Lau throws the ball and Nok Tok tries to catch it. He misses the ball and it lands on the ground. **"Oops!"**

3

"**Yojojo help Nok Tok! Bounce ball first.**" Yojojo bounces the ball on the ground to make it easy to catch. But Nok Tok misses the ball again.

4

"**De Li try help! Stand nearer.**" De Li stands closer to Nok Tok as she throws the ball, but he misses it again! Nok Tok is sad.

5 "Thinkapow! Use leaves to catch!" says Lau Lau. She gives Nok Tok two big leaves to catch the ball. But when she throws the ball, it bops him on the head! Nok Tok feels very silly.

6 When the cheebies come, Nok Tok tells them his problem. "I can't catch either," says one cheebie. This makes Nok Tok feel better. They can help each other learn!

7

The cheebie closes her eyes as she tries to catch the ball. That's why she misses! **"Open eyes, cheebie!"** he tells her. When Nok Tok goes next, the cheebie says, "You must open your eyes, too!"

8

Nok Tok didn't know his eyes were closed! The cheebie throws the ball to him, and Nok Tok makes sure to keep his eyes open. This time, he catches the ball. His friends helped him learn!

Waybuloo!

Pip Tips: Helping

In the story, **Nok Tok's** friends help him learn to catch the ball. Helping others makes the Piplings feel good! Do you like to help others, too?

Ask someone in your family if you can help with a task. When you have finished, make this badge! Put white paper over the star, then trace and colour it blue.

Ask a grown-up to help you cut it out and put a loop of tape on the back.

Happy Helper

Now wear your new badge ...
You're a star!

True Or False?

How well do you know the Piplings? Tick ✓ the things that are true, and cross ✗ the things that are false.

a **Lau Lau** has long ears.

b **Yojojo** looks like an elephant.

c **Nok Tok** wears a yellow shirt.

d The pink Pipling is called **Li De**.

Let's Play Peeka!

Lau Lau, Yojojo, De Li and Nok Tok are hiding in this picture. Can you find them all?

Narabug Dance

Lau Lau and the narabugs are dancing to Yojojo's music! How many narabugs can you count? Write the number in the box, then colour in the picture.

There are   narabugs.

Big Picture

These six close-ups can all be found in the big picture.
Draw a tick next to each one as you find it.

Anything Machine

frog

wheelbarrow

bird

Pipling pipes

blue narabug

25

Snack Time

Yojojo is hungry! Starting at number 1, join the dots to see his yummy snack, then colour it in.

Shadow Shapes

When the sun shines in Nara, **Nok Tok** can see his shadow! Can you match the picture of **Nok Tok** to his shadow?

a

b

c

Spot the Difference

These pictures look the same but 5 things are different in picture 2. Can you spot them all?

Lau Lau's Gift

1

One day, Lau Lau visits Nok Tok. His Anything Machine is turning fir cones into birdseed. **"Pretty fir cones!"** says Lau Lau. **"Nok Tok share fir cones with Lau Lau,"** he offers.

2

Lau Lau is so happy! She wants to give Nok Tok a gift in return. But what can she give? **"Give Nok Tok mangos for thank-you gift!"** De Li suggests.

3

Lau Lau thanks De Li for the good idea. Now she wants to give De Li a present for being so kind. She asks Yojojo for help. He is juggling apples with a cheebie. **"Give apples to De Li,"** suggests Yojojo. Lau Lau says yes!

4

Now Lau Lau wants to give everyone a gift! She calls her Pipling and cheebie friends together. She gives the mangos to the cheebies and the apples to the Piplings. But there is no more fruit left for Lau Lau!

5

"Thinkapow!" Nok Tok has an idea. "Cheebies and Piplings share." If they share the fruit, then everyone will get some!

6

The cheebies and Piplings cheer Nok Tok's clever idea. They know that sharing is fun. The cheebies put the mangos and apples into Nok Tok's Anything Machine.

7

Nok Tok puts a cup under the spout. Then he turns on the Anything Machine.

CREAK! CLANK!

The machine is working!

8

Suddenly, juice comes out of the spout. The Piplings and the cheebies happily drink the fruity juice. Mmm! It tastes so yummy because it was made by sharing!

Waybuloo!

Pip Tips: Sharing

In the story, the Piplings and cheebies share their fruit and make yummy juice for everybody. Sharing makes **Lau Lau** happy! Does sharing make you happy, too?

Share your toys or treats with a friend, brother or sister. Then put white paper over the star, then trace and colour it purple.

Ask a grown-up to help you cut it out and put a loop of tape on the back.

Super Sharer

Now wear your new badge ...
You're a star!

Tool Time

Nok Tok wants to make a birdhouse. Can you help him find his tools? Draw over the lines to finish the picture, then colour it in.

Flower Power

This caterpillar loves to smell **De Li's** pretty flowers. Find two flowers that are exactly the same and colour them in.

Pipling Puzzle

Nok Tok built a naracar to carry things for his friends. Which piece is missing from the naracar jigsaw picture?

a

b

c

Count It Out

Yojojo is playing with his Nara friends!
Count the number of each creature,
then draw a line to the correct number.

jumpybugs

stork

birds

caterpillars

1

2

3

4

Songbird

1

It is a beautiful day in Nara. Yojojo plays a song on his Pipling pipes. Suddenly, he hears a lovely sound up above.

2

It's a bird sitting in a tree. "Hi hi!" Yojojo says. He plays his pipes and the bird sings along. They make beautiful music together!

3

Yojojo is happy to make a new friend. When the bird flies down, he shuts it in a basket so it won't fly away. **"Pretty bird stay and sing for Yojojo."**

4

But when Yojojo plays his pipes again, the bird won't sing. He asks Nok Tok, De Li and Lau Lau for help. They give the bird flowers and berries, but it still won't sing.

5

When the cheebies come, Yojojo asks them for help. "Wild birds don't like being shut in baskets," they tell him. "They want to be free to fly and sing!"

6

Yojojo is sorry. He lets the bird fly away. Then he plays his pipes, but the bird does not come back. Yojojo is sad that his friend has gone.

7

"**Thinkapow!**" Yojojo has an idea. He brings whistles for all his friends. When they play a song together, the bird flies back and sings with them!

8

Working together has made the Piplings so happy that they float up in to the air. The cheebies cheer as the pretty bird flies up, too.

Waybuloo!

Pip Tips: Working Together

In the story, the Piplings and cheebies work together to bring back **Yojojo's** friend. Working together can make things easy and fun!

Work together with a friend or someone in your family on a puzzle in this annual. When you have finished, make this badge! Put white paper over the star, then trace and colour it orange.

Ask a grown-up to help you cut it out and put a loop of tape on the back.

Clever Cheebie

Now wear your new badge ... You're a star!

Tasty Treats

De Li's favourite treats are strawberries.
What's your favourite treat?
Draw it in this space!

Peeka Places

The cheebies are coming to play peeka! **Yojojo** and **De Li** run off to hide. Follow the wiggly lines with your finger to see where the Piplings are going.

bridge

garden

Music Match

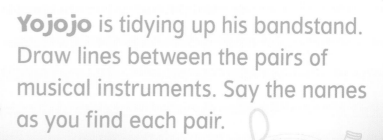

Yojojo is tidying up his bandstand. Draw lines between the pairs of musical instruments. Say the names as you find each pair.

trumpet

banjojo

banjojo

pipes

pipes

trumpet

47

Let's Do Yogo!

Yogo keeps the Piplings happy and healthy. Try to do it too!

Snail

Kneel down and reach back to hold your feet for a few seconds.

Candle

Lie on your back and raise your legs straight up. Now wiggle your feet!

Shell

Sit down and bring the bottoms of your feet together. Close your eyes and stay still for as long as you can.

Surfer

Stand with your feet wide apart, then twist your head and body to one side. Raise your arms to the sides and wiggle all over!

Counting Time

Yojojo is playing a new song on his whistle. Count the musical notes, then colour them in.

There are ⑤ musical notes.

Pipling Toolbox

Nok Tok is putting his tools in his toolbox. Can you tell which tool comes next in each row? Draw it in the box, then colour it in.

1

spanner   hammer   spanner   hammer

2

saw   rope   saw   rope

3

hammer   rope   hammer   rope

Make a Naracar

Nok Tok loves to drive around Nara.
Make a naracar just like **Nok Tok's!**

You will need:
an empty juice carton
a twig (about 7cm)
four large buttons
sticky tape
paint
a leaf
glue
paintbrush

1

Paint the juice carton in your favourite colour.

2

Glue the buttons along the bottom of the long edges of the carton for wheels.

3

Ask an adult to make a hole in the top front of the car. Poke the twig through the hole.

4

Tape the leaf to the twig. Now your naracar is just like **Nok Tok's!**

Colour the Piplings

Colour in this picture of the Piplings.
Draw yourself in the picture, too!

55

Tricky Kicky

1

Nok Tok is playing tricky kicky. He kicks the pod between two posts. **"Well done, Nok Tok!"** cheers De Li.

2

Yojojo and Lau Lau come to play. They ask De Li to join, but she is afraid she can't do it right. Finally, she tries to kick the pod. But it flies straight up to the sky!

3

The other Piplings tell De Li to keep trying, but now she is even more afraid. **"De Li can't play well,"** she says sadly.

4

The cheebies come and play tricky kicky with all the Piplings – except for De Li. They have lots of fun!

5

One of the cheebies sees that De Li is afraid. She gives her a pebble and says, "This is a lucky pebble. It will help you play tricky kicky!"

6

De Li holds the pebble and kicks the pod. It rolls right between the posts ... **GOAL!** She is so glad to have the lucky pebble!

7

De Li goes to take another kick, but she drops her lucky pebble! She can't find it anywhere. The kind cheebie tells her, "Don't worry, De Li. You don't need luck!"

8

"De Li can do it!" says De Li. She takes a big kick ... and scores another goal! Her friends give a big cheer and she smiles happily. **"Now De Li not afraid to try any more!"**

Story Quiz

In the story, **De Li** has fun trying to play tricky kicky. Can you remember the answers to these questions? Circle the answers, then check the story to see if you're right!

1 What is **De Li** trying to kick?

 vase

 pod

 trowel

2 Who did **De Li** see first in the story?

 Lau Lau

 Yojojo

 Nok Tok

3 What did the cheebie give **De Li** for luck?

 pebble

 flower

 paintbrush

Neepnip Nibble

Narabugs love neepnips! Which neepnip has **De Li's** narabug been nibbling?

a

b

c

d

Pipling Treasure Hunt

The Piplings are on a treasure hunt!

Lau Lau

3 Paints

2 paintbrush

6 pot

Yojojo

5 watering can

1 banjojo

3 drums

You Will Need:
A dice; three counters for each player

How to Play: Play this game with up to three friends. Choose which Pipling you want to be. Take it in turns to throw the dice. If the number beside one of your treasures shows, put a counter on the picture. The first player to put counters on all three of their treasures is the winner!

Nok Tok

5 basket

1 spanner

4 saw

De Li

6 flower

2 wheelbarrow

4 fork

Cheebie Treasures

Here's a treasure hunt for you! Can you point to three things that begin with the letter **b**?

banjojo

bucket

basket

Guess Who?

These two Piplings are playing peeka with you! Guess who they are by reading the clues.

This Pipling is the colour blue. He likes to make and mend things too!

This Pipling is

N_____

This Pipling's ears are very long. She loves to dance to every song!

This Pipling is

L_____

Colour Code

Colour in the picture, using
the colour code to help you.

Bye Bye, Cheebie!

The Piplings had lots of fun with you! They're so happy that they're floating up into the air.

waybuloo!

See you soon, cheebie!

Answers

p12: Odd One Out
Picture c is the odd one out.
Yojojo is missing his tail.

p13: Picture Present

p15: Garden Guess
Row 1 – banana, row 2 –
carrobeet, row 3 – plumato.

p21: True or False
a and c are true, b and d are false.

p23: Narabug Dance
There are 3 narabugs.

p24-25: Big Picture

p26: Snack Time
Yojojo's snack is a banana.

p27: Shadow Shapes
Shadow b matches Nok Tok.

p28: Spot the Difference
The banjojo and stork are missing,

De Li has replaced Nok Tok,
Yojojo has a whistle, the tulip is red.

p35: Time for Yogo
Nok Tok should take path c.

p38: Pipling Puzzle
Piece a is missing.

p39: Count It Out
There are 3 jumpybugs,
1 stork, 4 birds and 2 caterpillars.

p47: Music Match

p50: Counting Time
There are 5 musical notes.

p51: Pipling Toolbox

Row 1 – spanner, row 2 – saw,
row 3 – hammer.

p60: Story Quiz
1 – pod, 2 – Nok Tok, 3 – pebble.

p61: Neepnip Nibble
Neepnip b has been nibbled.

P65: Guess Who?
The Piplings are Nok Tok and
Lau Lau.

Welcome to Waybuloo™
Books from Egmont

Join the Piplings in their Nara adventures
egmont.co.uk/waybuloo

**Find the Piplings!
Peek Through Book
£4.99**

**Waybuloo Pocket Library
£4.99**

**The Wonder of Waybuloo
Sticker Activity Book
£3.99**

Over 100 stickers inside!

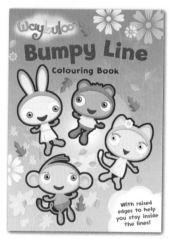

**Waybuloo Bumpy Line
Colouring Book
£3.99**

With raised edges to help you stay inside the lines!

**Waybuloo Story Book
Showtime!
£3.99**

As Seen on TV

**Waybuloo Story Book
Moving Things
£3.99**

As Seen on TV

**Yojojo's Happy Happy Song
Sound Book
£5.99**

**Waybuloo Stencil
Play Book
£5.99**

With 5 stencil sheets and 16 play pieces!